"For you, the city, thus I turn my back:
There is a world elsewhere."

Coriolanus, Act 3 Scene 3

Titles in Dark Reads:

Badger Publishing Limited, Oldmedow Road, Hardwick Industrial Estate, King's Lynn PE30 4JJ
Telephone: 01438 791037

www.badgerlearning.co.uk

DANNY PEARSON

Illustrated by Aleksandar Sotirovski

Titan ISBN 978-1-78464-445-1

Publisher: Susan Ross
Senior Editor: Danny Pearson
Editorial Coordinator: Claire Morgan
Copyeditor: Cheryl Lanyon
Designer: Bigtop Design Ltd
Illustrator: Aleksandar Sotirovski

2 4 6 8 10 9 7 5 3 1

Contents

CHAPTER 1
PLANET TITAN

Planet Titan was slowly dying.

Its leaders knew it.

Its people knew it.

They had run out of the fuel needed to power their machines.

They needed more, and they needed to find it quickly.

Titan's leaders drew up a plan. The plan was to invade the closest planet to them – Planet Antium. They had the fuel that Titan needed.

The leaders called upon their greatest fighter. He was young but strong. His name was Mar.

He would lead the army to Antium and take their fuel.

Mar led the army to Planet Antium.

Titan's army was too strong for Antium.
The war was short and bloody.

Mar took all of Antium's fuel and left their
king, King Auf, and the people of the planet
with nothing.

Mar returned to Titan a hero.

Titan now had fuel and could power their
machines again.

CHAPTER 2
CORRO

Mar was rewarded with a medal and made a Lord. He was the youngest Lord in the galaxy.

He was also given a new hero's name. He was now known as Corro.

Corro wanted more power though. He wanted to be a High Lord.

The only way to become a High Lord was for the people to vote for him.

Some of Titan's leaders were afraid of Corro and did not want him to become too powerful.

They spread lies about him, which the people started to believe.

When the vote came, Corro lost.

Corro was very angry. He had saved Titan and this was how he was rewarded.

Corro vowed revenge upon the people. He threw his medal away and boarded his space ship.

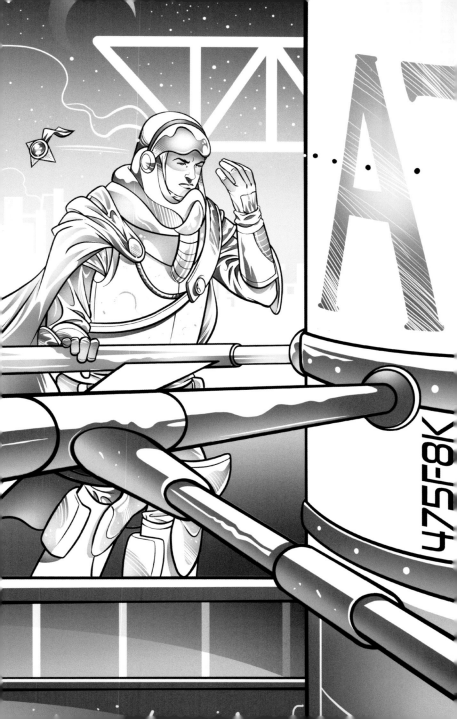

CHAPTER 3
BETRAYAL

Corro flew his space ship back to Antium. He wanted to meet the defeated king.

King Auf was shocked to see Corro and was about to kill him when Corro told him his plan.

Corro told King Auf how he felt betrayed and that he would do anything to make Titan pay.

He had a plan to take back the stolen fuel and he asked King Auf to help.

CHAPTER 4
REVENGE

King Auf agreed to the plan.

He knew Corro was a great fighter and was his best hope of getting Antium's fuel back.

Corro and King Auf took an army to
Planet Titan.

Corro knew all Titan's weaknesses and
damaged the main shield protecting it.

The planet was theirs for the taking.

The army of Antium invaded the planet easily and took back their fuel.

The people of the capital city begged Corro to stop but he just laughed in their faces.

He was teaching them a lesson. He was getting his revenge.

CHAPTER 5
FINAL BATTLE

After King Auf had taken all of the fuel back he invited Corro back to his main ship. He had a gift for him.

"Corro, you have served us well. With the planet's shield down we now give you the honour of destroying it."

King Auf invited him to push the button that would destroy his home world.

It was too much for Corro.

He had wanted to teach the people of Titan a lesson but he didn't want to destroy them.

He could not bring himself to blow up the planet and refused to press the button.

King Auf now felt betrayed. He ordered his best soldiers to surround Corro.

A tear rolled down Corro's cheek. He knew this was the end.

The soldiers moved in.

STORY FACTS

This story was inspired by William Shakespeare's play Coriolanus, which was published in 1623. It is set in Ancient Rome.

This Shakespeare play was turned into a film which was set in modern-day Rome. Coriolanus was played by the actor Ralph Fiennes who also played Lord Voldemort in the *Harry Potter* film series.

Titan was also inspired by science fiction films such as *Star Wars*, which was first released in 1977.

QUESTIONS

What is happening to Planet Titan?
(page 7)

What is the name of the planet that Mar invades?
(page 8)

What hero name is Mar given?
(page 12)

Why don't people vote for Corro to become a High Lord?
(page 14)

What does King Auf invite Corro to do?
(page 24)

Danny Pearson was very much a child of the 80s. He was brought up on a diet of unusual cartoons and movies involving things changing into other things, or adventures set to cheap keyboard soundtracks.

He has worked on hundreds of publications for teachers and students.

MEET THE ARTIST

Aleksandar Sotirovski is from Macedonia. He is an illustrator with over 25 years' experience. He has worked on lots of children's books, textbooks and posters. He is also a concept artist for comics and games.